The first Chance Lighthouse as exhibited
at the Great Exhibition of 1851

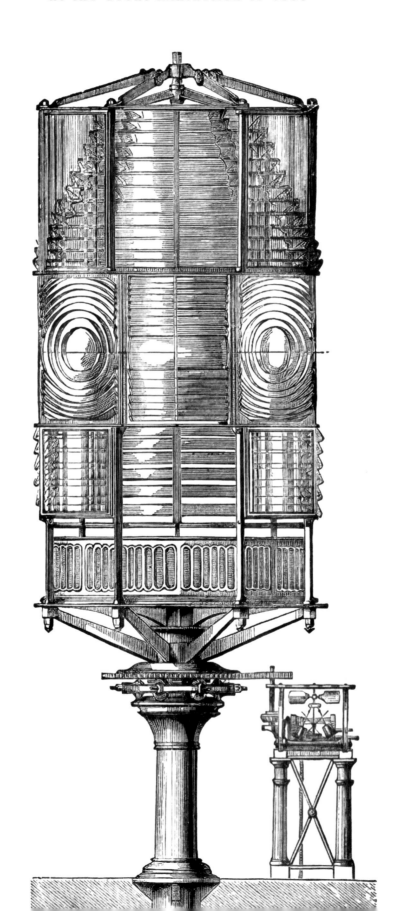

MIRROR FOR

Chance

Published in the Year of the
Festival of Britain 1951

Reprinted for the
Chance Brothers Bicentenary, 1822-2022

CHANCE BROTHERS LIMITED, SMETHWICK, ENGLAND

PUBLISHED BY CHANCE HERITAGE TRUST

www.chanceht.org

9 780956 809629

foreword

Despite the Chance Brothers glassworks closing down for good in the 1980s, interest in the company has remained consistently strong, and continues in strength to this day. No doubt this is in part because of a personal connection for people whose family members - or they themselves - worked at Chances.

There are also the reminders of the legacy created by Chance Brothers itself, and by members of the Chance family, notably West Smethwick Park, recently renovated with the addition of a new state-of-the-art pavilion which replaced the long-gone and much missed café. A number of schools, recreation grounds, churches, hospitals, war memorials and parks benefited from the philanthropy of Chances, as well as the University of Birmingham where there is a Chance Professor of Engineering.

The reach of Chance Brothers extended beyond its first home in Smethwick, with the chemical works in Oldbury, another factory in Glasgow pioneering the manufacture and uses of fibreglass, a branch operation in Malvern, and even a secret factory in St Helens, which was a joint venture with Pilkington Brothers immediately before the Second World War to meet the growing need for military optical glass.

Worldwide, of course, there are all the Chance lighthouses - thousands of them - which winked at the edges of the oceans, lakes and seaways of every corner of the globe. Many of them still retain their Victorian-era Chance lens, revolving every day for over a century, and it would be impossible to work out how many lives and how many tonnes of shipping have been saved because of them.

However, I suspect that much of the interest in Chance Brothers is the result of the diligent care they afforded their workers, and the lingering effect that has in societal memory. Employees were treated less as units and more as members of a great family. The measures undertaken by the management in healthcare, pension benefits, child labour, safety at work, leisure and entertainment, literacy and education were pioneering, and predated similar introductions by the Welfare State by decades.

Mirror for Chance was produced when Chance Brothers was close to the culmination of a long take-over by Pilkington Brothers by mutual consent, but was still being run as a thriving and expanding business with Sir Hugh Chance as Chairman. Produced in the year of the Festival of Britain and the centenary of the Lighthouse Department, it was a showcase for the heritage and innovation of a proud glassmaker which was once the world's largest.

Henry Chance
Middleton Court, nr Ludlow
October 2022

Henry is Vice Chairman of the Chance Heritage Trust and a descendant
of Lucas and William Chance: the original "Brothers"

PROLOGUE

The blob of soft glass swells into a bubble, glowing deeply red, catching a fiercer light from the nearby furnace mouth. The glassblower spins his pipe, blowing with distended cheeks, and swings the bulb, and blows again. His movements are rhythmic, unhurried, almost casual. . . . Can it be quite as easy as it seems?

The glassblower lays aside his pipe and takes a second one, generously wets the mouthpiece, spins and blows and swings. . . . Behind and to one side of him hang other pipes in the cooling racks, where the waste 'moil' as it contracts sounds like a ragged fusillade of pistol shots. Behind and to the other side are the furnaces, throwing their bars of heat across the way. The shop seems dark after the daylight outside. Fragments crunch under foot. Dozens of dark figures are moving to and fro . . . tending the furnaces, lending their weight to the levers of presses, lifting hot metal in asbestos gloves. A trolley-load of globes goes by, and with it a hot breath. Steam hisses up from a blower's mould. . . . This is a scene which never loses its fascination, even when you know all the why's and wherefore's even when you have known for ten, twenty, forty, or as long as a hundred and twenty-nine years.

For more than a century and a quarter we at Chance Brothers have been glass makers, and for much of that time precision engineers. From glass we came to lighthouses and from lighthouses to engineering, with a steady selective logic. In the course of our history we have grown from a small manufacture to a big modern industry, as many another business has done.

But . . . side by side with the robot perfection of machinery, with the endless ribbons of glass, with the complex organization of large-scale production and marketing, with the change, experiment, invention, adoption, adaptation, research and replacement which is continually going on . . . there stands the glassblower, just as he did in 1822 and long before. He is no sentimental relic, but a man whose art only is more ancient than those of his fellows on the mass-production lines, in the draughtsman's office or the engineering shop. Like them he fits into a pattern in a world of special skills, where the simplest tools and the most ingenious machines are the instruments of the men who devise and control them, and not gods to be served.

That is the sort of thing we have in mind when we tell people that our business has a character of its own.

The process of making sheet glass, from the marvering
(front-right) to the spinning of the sheet (rear-left).

INTERIOR OF A CROWN-GLASS HOUSE

contents

since 1824

SINCE EIGHTEEN TWENTY-TWO

In November 1822, Robert Lucas Chance became the owner of the works of the British Crown Glass Company and other property at Smethwick, comprising altogether some fifteen acres of what had, earlier, been "Blakeley's Farm". Thereupon he wrote to his brother Henry, a barrister at Lincoln's Inn: "I have every reason for thinking that the concern will realize the most sanguine expectations I have form'd", and the words, for all their stiffness, give a hint of the writer's excitement.

As it turned out, the occasion was in fact momentous, both for Blakeley's Farm and its new proprietor. The business founded on the 18th of May still centres on those fifteen acres, but it has developed to an extent which even the most sanguine expectations could hardly have foreseen. Spon Lane has an atmosphere no longer even remotely rustic. Yet nothing which has happened at Chances' since 1822 runs counter to the broad lines of Robert Lucas's strategy as evidenced by the early years of his personal management.

It is always an easy matter to prophesy backwards: to see with the disenchanted wisdom of the 1950s, what golden opportunities offered to men at the beginning of the industrial nineteenth century. It is quite another gift, rare then as now, to recognize such opportunities before they have become history. In describing people like Robert Lucas Chance, who combined precisely that sort of acumen with the energy to make use of it, it is hardly good enough to say that they were characteristic of their age. In the outcome, the age was characteristic of them.

Lucas Chance possessed energy and initiative, of a kind which enabled him to help manage his father's Birmingham hardware business from the age of fourteen. He also had the art of learning quickly, for his whole apprenticeship in glass was contained in the four years he had spent at the Nailsea glass works of which his father was for some years part owner. And he certainly had courage, for he took over the British Crown Glass Company's business at a time when British glassmakers suffered under duties and restrictions so burdensome that even to-day they might be quoted as a warning to bureaucrats. Not only was the notorious window tax still in force, but no less than five perspiring excise officers brooded day and night over the pots at Spon Lane, besides an inspector whose only duty it was to see that the others were not bribed.

Glassworkers in the mid-eighteenth century, from a
contemporary French manual

It was not simply that- Lucas Chance foresaw the inevitable failure of such a complicated system ot strangula-tion: he took the steps to hasten its end. In 1831 we find him heading a deputation to the Chancellor of the Excheq-uer to fight the window tax. In 1843 we come across him quietly superintending the building ot a new glasshouse (his sixth). in anticipation of the trade recovery which he knew would follow the repeal of the excise duties. when that happened—as he expected—in 1845.

Nor was there. on the other hand. anything monotonous about his success. He had the temperament to make quick decisions. and with them to make mistakes: while in the glass trade itself there were booms and depressions beyond his control. and formidable technical difficulties to be overcome in the constant struggle against foreign competition. Early in his career there was a setback (due to an association with an inventor appropriately named Badams) which might have been fatal. but for the intervention of his brother William. who joined the partnership in 1832. The two branches of the family have been represented in the business from that day to this.

By character these brothers were natural foils to each other: Lucas Chance inventive. venturesome. quick to anticipate. William more cautious and stable. It was Lucas who. in the face of opposition from his partners. first brought to Smethwick the great French authority Georges Bontemps. and thus established in England. in the 1830s. that manufacture of sheet glass in which the Continent was already expert: with Bontemps' help French workmen. recruited and imported for the purpose. were installed in a special glasshouse. known for many years after their departure as the "French house". The experiment was triumphant in the end. though the foreigners were a great cause of trouble with their high wages. their high-handed behaviour. their idleness and their huge reluctance to impart the secrets of their craft to any but their own blood relations.

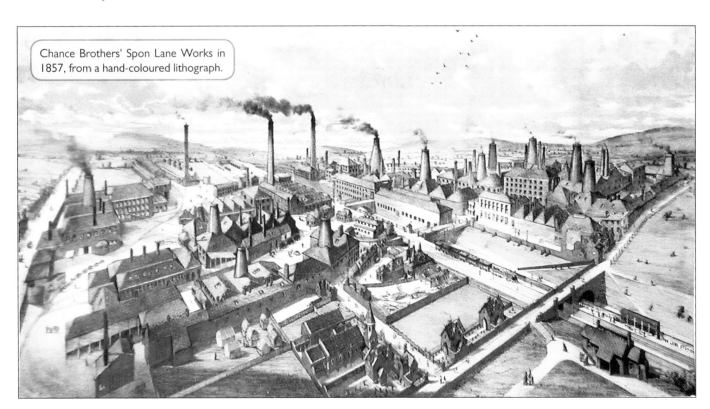

Chance Brothers' Spon Lane Works in 1857, from a hand-coloured lithograph.

Bontemps, a brilliant man and for many years a valued colleague of the two Chances and their early partners, bore only the first in the list of great names with which Chance Brothers have been associated in the course of their history—names such as Faraday, Bessemer, Crookes, Siemens and Hopkinson. But it has surely already been made clear that all the brains in this business were not imported: if any further evidence were required, Sir James Timmins Chance might be called upon to provide it.

The son of William, nephew of Robert Lucas, James Timmins Chance seemed able to combine the solid judgment of the one with the rapid judgment of the other, and to add to the combination a genius distinctly his own. A mathematician of eminence (he was the Seventh Wrangler of his year), a classical scholar, a theologian, an able engineer and by first choice a lawyer, having once entered the family firm he was bound to leave his mark on it. From the first of January 1839, when he was admitted to partnership (the firm had just adopted the style of "Chance Brothers & Co."), to the first of January 1889, when he retired (as the Company added the word "Limited"), he was an inspiration to the business and incalculably influenced its development. But for his interest and knowledge, it is possible that the association between Chance Brothers and navigation lighting, which has endured and flourished now for a hundred years, would never have come about. But for Chances* early lighthouse venture there might—who knows? —have been no Chance Engineering. . . . Histories are full of unanswerable questions.

The Lighthouse Works at Spon Lane date from the year 1851, the year of the Great Exhibition, to which the partners sent the first lighthouse optic they ever made (. . . a century later the beam from another Chance light was to shine for the Festival of Britain). But Chance did much more than that for Paxton's phenomenal Crystal Palace. From Spon Lane, within a few months, came all its crystal—close on a million square feet of glass.

A view of the Great Exhibition. The great structure, glazed with Chance sheet glass, is seen in its first setting between the Serpentine and the Row.

THE CRYSTAL PALACE IN HYDE PARK FOR GRAND INTERNATIONAL EXHIBITION OF 1851.
Dedicated to the Royal Commissioners

1. An Australian lighthouse installed by Chance Brothers in 1878.

2. 1914–18: Chance searchlight lenses in action.

3. 1939–45: An A.A. Rangefinder fitted with an optical system of Chance glass.

When the achievements of more than a hundred years pass by in rapid review, it is quite startling to notice how early are some other of Chances' 'foundation' dates. Paper-thin glass for microscopy, for instance, was first made at Smethwick in 1840, and for forty years after was made nowhere else in the world. Lucas Chance took out his first patent for optical glass in 1838, to start manufacture, with Bontemps' help, ten years later. Rolled plate glass was developed in the '50s, spectacle glass in the '70s, and figured rolled in the '80s. Heat-resisting glass, however, the forerunner of to-day's Hysil, was a graduate of the 1914-18 war, when the sudden dearth of foreign supplies brought urgent demands upon Chance.

That is the way of wars. Chance optical glass, for instance, was for years and years a hopelessly uneconomic proposition for the Company, confronted as they were by subsidized German competition and the carefully fostered legend of German supremacy. If all that time they carried on with research and manufacture—as they did—their only encouragement was an obstinate belief in their own product . . . until suddenly, in 1914, Britain discovered that she was the possessor of an optical glass industry which, if small in scale, was equal in quality to any in the world. In the inter-war years some Government support was forthcoming, and 1939 found Chance Brothers ready to expand and to meet successfully the demands of a new emergency.

Of Chance in the Second World War so much might be said that it can hardly be attempted. Suffice it to record that Chance glass supplied most of the lenses for hundreds of thousands of gunsights, rangefinders, aerial cameras and periscopes as well as a wide variety of specialist equipment, from the small glass heads used in preserving blood serum to penicillin flasks and radar tubes, airfield lights and optical colour filter glasses.

It is also rather the way of wars to absorb more than their fair share of attention in a history of everyday things. War times, often enough, are forcing times for ideas which have been slowly growing during less disturbed years. If the long period of industrial development in rhe latter half of the nineteenth century cannot compete for drama with the twentieth, that is not to say that it was less important. . . .

You will find the substance of both in the following pages.

SPEAKING FOR CHANCE BROTHERS

CHAIRMAN

SIR HUGH CHANCE.

A great-grandson of William Chance, the brother and partner of the Founder. He joined the firm in 1920 and was elected a Managing Director in 1924 and Chairman in 1947. He was knighted in 1945 for services to education.

MANAGING DIRECTOR

.JOHN RAYMOND. M.I.E.E..

A New Zealander by birth, he was educated in this country, and before joining Chance Brothers in 1938 held various industrial appointments. He was elected a Director in 1940. Joint Managing Director in 1941 and Managing Director in 1946.

GENERAL MANAGERS

H. L. BARMAN,

    Engineering Division, who is also **Deputy Managing Director**.

W. M. HAMPTON. PhD., B.Sc., F.Inst.P., F.I.E.S., F.R.I.C., Optical and Special Glass Division, who is also **Technical Director**.

C. J. S. NEWMAN

    Flat Glass Division

R. WRATHALL, O.B.E.,

    Blown and Pressed Glass Division

SECRETARY AND CHIEF ACCOUNTANT

L. H. CLEAVER. A.C.A.

SENIOR MANAGERS

J. A. AITCHISON	Manager, Glasgow Works
W. E. BARRETT	Chief Engineer
J. W. CHANCE	London Manager
HAMILTON FULTON	Export Manager

SALES MANAGERS

F. W. BEAUMONT	Lighthouse Works
J. B. W. BROWNSDON	Blown and Pressed Glass
T. O. ORR	Sumo Pumps Ltd
W. N. WHEAT. M.B.E.	Optical and Special Glass
A. E. WRIGHT. M.C.	Flat Glass

AREA EXPORT MANAGERS

W. E. SKILBECK   British Commonwealth and Turkey

T. A. S. GREEN North, Central and South America, Caribbean area, Spain and Portugal

H. V. SKAN   Europe and the rest of the world

SECRETARY AND CHIEF ACCOUNTANT

CHAIRMAN AND BOARD OF DIRECTORS

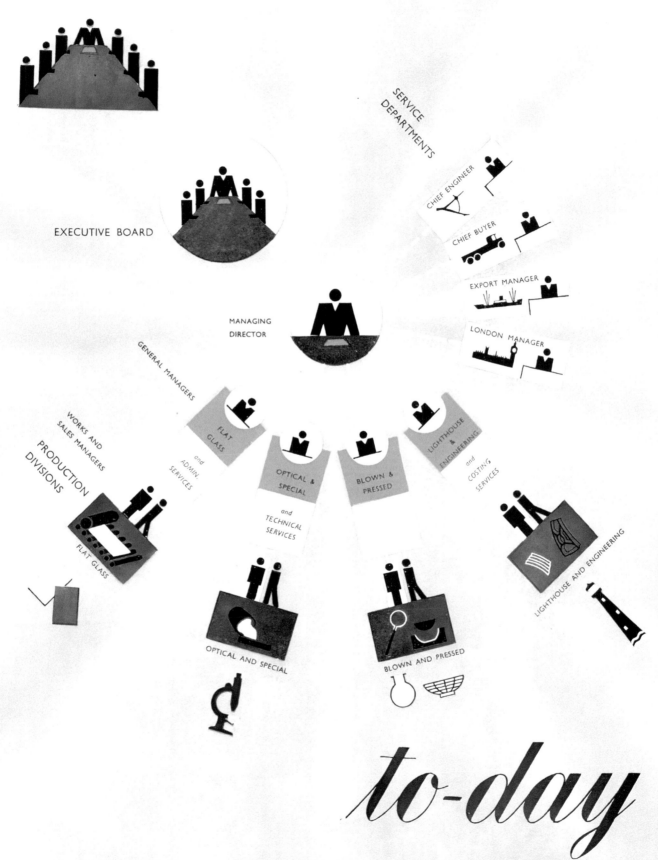

SERVICE DEPARTMENTS

CHIEF ENGINEER

CHIEF BUYER

EXPORT MANAGER

LONDON MANAGER

EXECUTIVE BOARD

MANAGING DIRECTOR

GENERAL MANAGERS

WORKS AND SALES MANAGERS

PRODUCTION DIVISIONS

FLAT GLASS and ADMIN. SERVICES

OPTICAL & SPECIAL

BLOWN & PRESSED

LIGHTHOUSE & ENGINEERING and COSTING SERVICES

and TECHNICAL SERVICES

FLAT GLASS

OPTICAL AND SPECIAL

BLOWN AND PRESSED

LIGHTHOUSE AND ENGINEERING

to-day

"CHANCES'" TO-DAY

You will have noticed, on page 7, a print showing the Glass Works at Spon Lane as they appeared in the year 1857, when Chance Brothers was thirty-three years old. If you took that print in your hand and walked into the works to-day through one of the three main entrances, you could find your way about quite easily with its help—provided you managed to lull the suspicions of the gatekeeper.

This is to say that in general plan, though new-looking buildings line many of its thoroughfares, and modern equipment is everywhere to be seen, "Chances'" is "Chances'" still. The massive, brick-built cones which rose above the old furnaces have gone, it is true. Hayricks stand no more behind the School (though people still speak of "the Rickyard"). But the main layout is the same, with canal and railway, side by side, cutting their way through the centre of the Works.

The old Hall, part country house, part farmhouse (and now transformed within to a modern drawing office), occupies its familiar niche beside the level crossing . . . the bell in its cupola over the Seven-Storey Building still causes late arrivals to break into a trot . . . the old school block holds its ground, doing duty as a canteen, a hostel and a club. That little bridge which crosses the canal is the selfsame Hartley Bridge which the Founder named in honour of his first partner, only now it glimmers blue in the sunshine, the clear blue of the fleet of lorries and vans that shuttle to and fro— Chance blue, the colour of to-day.

Turning to the print once more, you look in vain for the huge overhead runway cranes, the Wellsian complex of vertical retorts and tubes for gas production, even the flagstaff . . . can that be modern, too Where, then, are the 'Glassmaker's Rest' and the cottages in Scotch Row? . . . Why, *they* were pulled down in the 1840s, and so can figure in neither print nor present. This is what comes of accumulated history. In a sense nothing dies—while no development, however new, seems unexpected.

At some such point as this it is a good idea to pause for refreshment, and clear your mind by talking about politics or golf—because the scene inside the glasshouses, modern though the equipment may be, busy and businesslike the tempo, carries the same uncanny undertones of generations past, only this time as much of the whole British glass industry as of Chance Brothers. No craft in the world is so fascinating to watch as modern glassmaking . . . but after lunch . . . the blend of then and now is a little rich for an empty stomach.

At Smethwick to-day the very terms in use conjoin modern engineering, the local idiom and old French. Many of the men you meet, given whiskers and billycock hats, could sit for portraits of their great-grandfathers, though the mass-production and continuous-production plant they control would have amazed those ancestors. And if this atmosphere is less noticeable in the Sumo and Austinlite shops, in the Lighthouse Works it becomes as pervasive as a sea mist.

An overhead runway crane
for handling raw materials

The men and women who work for Chances' of Smethwick for the most part belong to Smethwick—many, indeed, to Spon Lane—and that through generations. These are the Black Country folk, who would be rather less offended to be taken for Burmese than for Birminghamites. Their voices are distinct, their traditions permanent, their loyalties obstinate, and their sense of humour very much their own. The hobbies they choose are those of countrymen. The skills they wield are a heritage. They name their children after minor prophets.

Although the Company still takes pride in the friendly tradition that characterises its relationship with employees, and in its close personal contacts with many customers, it is no longer a strictly family business. It has become, in the course of time, a wide organization, with branch factories at Glasgow, St. Helens and Malvern, with a London office in St. James's

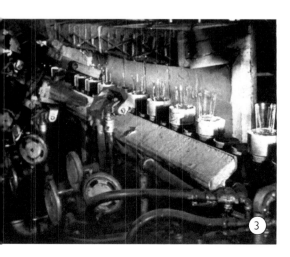

1. Weighing raw materials for 'batch' in the Flat Glass Division; the exact balance of a formula depends upon accurate measurement

2. Automatic batch feeder harnessed to a 24-hour tank furnace. The contents of such a tank represent, at any moment of the day or night, all stages in the creation of glass from its raw materials.

3. Glass tumblers on an automatic fire-polishing machine. Brilliance is imparted to a glass article, after contact with a mould, by re-melting the surface in flames of controlled intensity

Square and agents in most capitals of the world. And yet the heart of the matter belongs to those early acres in Smethwick which once were farmland, where pride in "Chances'" is a kind of patriotism.

A WINDOW IN ST. JAMES'S SQUARE . . .

Chance Brothers have the only shop-window in St. James's Square, London . . . at number 28, on the south side. Behind (and above) that window they do much business—for this is London Office, with its quadruple function of Area Sales Headquarters, Information Desk, Conference Centre and Reception Bureau to the whole Chance organization.

Each of the Manufacturing Divisions keeps its special representative here, in close touch with customers in London and the Home Counties, in even closer touch with Smethwick by teleprinter. Information is provided for users of Chance glass, such as architects and industrial chemists. Export enquiries from London business houses are dealt with, and every other sort of enquiry, too.

The people at London Office undertake the reception of overseas visitors, arranging hotel accommodation for them, visits to the Works, very often recreation as well. They provide a similar (if modified) service for Chance Brothers' own executive staff when they come up to town. They organize meetings with customers in the panelled Conference Room with its eighteenth century furniture . . . meetings over which the Founder and his partner-brother preside in benevolent silence, for their portraits hang on opposing walls, in line with the long table.

Then there is the public relations side . . . for London Office also handles publicity matters and is responsible for press advertising, printed literature, exhibition stands, etc., and for editorial publicity as well.

All this goes on at 28 St. James's Square, London, S.W.1. On page 71 there's a map which shows you how to get there.

LONDON OFFICE
28 St. James's Square. London. S.W.1

. . . AND A DOORWAY ON THE WORLD

The Export Department at Chance Brothers is comparatively young: it serves the three Glass Divisions. but. not the specialist Engineering Division. which continues to look after its own export interests.

The existence of this new department doesn't mean that export business is new to Chance—very far from it. It is a comment upon the tremendous increase which that business has shown in recent years. Exports now total more than 25 per cent of the Company's turnover: while the entire output for the Group a few years ago was less than the export figure is to-day for the Glass Works alone.

Add to this the value of Chances' indirect exports . . . in cameras and optical instruments. headlight lenses. Crookes glass for spectacles, industrial components and so on . . . and the grand total becomes impressive.

The Export Department separates its world into three zones (roughly speaking. the British Commonwealth. the Western Hemisphere. Europe and the rest) and operates through a network of Agents in more than seventy-five markets. In the U.S.A.. where Chance Brothers have done business for some eighty years. facilities have been extended recently by the establishment of Sumo Pumps. Inc.. at Stamford. Connecticut. Apart from everyday communication. interest is stimulated by overseas visits from members of the Company. who in the past three years have covered more than 400.000 miles (or sixteen times round the world).

Chance Brothers Export Service exists to serve. Both at London Office and at Spon Lane. Smethwick. they are delighted to receive visits or enquiries from abroad.

Loading a lorry with flat glass crated for export

Engineering apprentices in the Drawing Office

Learning how to manage a lathe

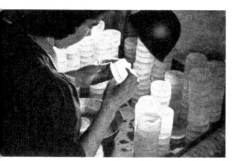
Examining optical blanks

The Canteen and Social Club building

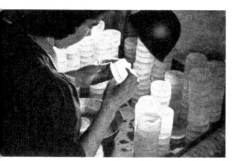
The Medical Centre

WORKING FOR CHANCE

When a lad in his middle 'teens comes straight from school to work at Spon Lane, he sees it all with a fresh, inquisitive eye, untroubled by history. And what he discovers is an allegiance to be proud of, a great range of skills to be mastered, a career with opportunities for a lifetime and a community to which he henceforth belongs. Not a little.

Chance Brothers, naturally, employ many more experienced hands than beginners. All told, there are now some 3,500 people working for Chance, and a high proportion have technical mastery of a kind which doesn't come after twelve months, or twelve years for that matter . . . at the moment of writing there are no less than twenty-six with more than fifty years service behind each of them. But fifty years ago even these hands were new—and the future of the industry lies with the young.

Nowadays people in employment (and notably young people) are protected by law from exploitation. Law, in these matters, follows public opinion. Chance Brothers have been helping to shape public opinion ever since the Company was founded. During the 111th century, for example, the partners built and endowed a private school on their premises for the children of their employees (at the time an almost revolutionary undertaking), and now that general education has become the country's responsibility, Chance can still show the way in technical training and opportunity.

Not every lad is fitted for a straight glassmaking or engineering apprenticeship. The Company's training scheme is flexibly planned to allow scope for individual aptitudes, so that each boy can at the very least equip himself for later life, and at the best travel as far as his talents will take him.

The Personnel Manager keeps an interested eye on all these youngsters (and keeps in touch with their parents). His is a job with countless sidelines, among them the editorship of *Chance Comments*, a magazine with accredited correspondents throughout the Works, which provides a welcome bi-monthly review of social and sporting news, together with feature articles, reports from the Works Consultative Committee, photographs, cartoons, anecdotes, reminiscences. Welfare is also his concern—a word familiar in every modern industry, though it does not always mean the same thing.

Any description of welfare at Chance Brothers reads like an enthusiastic catalogue. It covers, for instance a well equipped Medical Centre dealing not only with the day-to-day injuries which occur in all factories, but also with the treatment of minor ills and rehabilitation of the injured and sick. It includes a Works Hostel, as a short-term solution to modern housing difficulties . . . a Staff Hostel as well. It means, also, canteens providing 175,000 hot meals a year . . . a Youth Club . . . a Social and Recreation Club with 3,000 members, whose various tastes are catered for by nineteen specialist sections, ranging from angling and other outdoor pastimes to music appreciation and drama . . . Adjoining the thirty-two acres of the Smethwick factory are sixteen of playing fields.

Working for Chance certainly means working for Chance. But that has never been merely a matter of clocking in and out.

RESEARCH

Scientific research is an essential of modern industry. Many manufacturing companies run their own independent research units, and some of these have a usefulness and authority which go beyond the demands of a particular business or even industry. Chance research fits such a picture naturally enough . . .

In that hardworking, turbulent, hit-or-miss period of industrial growth the nineteenth century, industrial research was, however, not usually organized in specialist teams such as we hear about to-day. Men of wide independent genius flourished, like Faraday and Davy and Fresnel, but only the exceptional business knew how to co-operate with them. Chance Brothers was one.

When James Timmins Chance first met Michael Faraday, in 1845, the latter was an international figure. By contrast, Dr. John Hopkinson, though Senior Wrangler in 1871, may be said to have started his world reputation with Chance Brothers when he took over the management of the Lighthouse Works a year later. Like Faraday, Sir William Crookes came upon the scene an already celebrated authority. Like Hopkinson, Sir William Siemens and Sir Henry Bessemer (as they were later to become) were young men, comparatively unknown, when their respective inventions were the subject of investigation at Spon Lane. There were many others, with names only less well known to-day.

Siemens's regenerative furnace of 1861 succeeded, in spite of its inventor's doubts. Bessemer's plate glass process of 1846, for all its inventor's confidence, did not. . . yet it foreran modern methods. Chance Crookes glass gave a lead in industrial sight-protection which the Company still hold. It was through the help and encouragement of Faraday and others that Chance Brothers were able to take on the manufacture of complete coastal lights, instead of confining themselves to the glass components with which they started.

The present-day Research Laboratory at Spon Lane has its origins in the First World War, and in the demand which then suddenly confronted Chance for optical and heat-resisting glasses most of which had previously come from abroad. Its organization to-day exemplifies the double function which scientific research performs for industry. Two of its three sections, the Chemical and Physical Laboratories, are first and foremost, Control Laboratories—they see to the maintenance of standards. The third, the Research and Development Laboratory, as its name implies, is chiefly concerned with new glasses and new processes: it is this, with its experimental meltings and pilot plants, which stands for research as the layman knows the term.

From it have come in recent years, many valuable developments. As a result, for instance, of its investigations, the present platinum melting section of the Optical and Special Glass Division came into being, and with it glass of such optical properties as has gladdened the hearts of the makers of photographic lenses. (And here present-day research takes over, in a sense, from Faraday, who a hundred and twenty years ago made a similar attempt, but could not carry it beyond the laboratory stage.)

Of a quite different nature was the evolution, recently, of a formula which at last makes possible a true comparison of the thermal efficiencies of all glass tank melting furnaces, most useful to the industry in this country.

As different again was the enquiry which, beginning as a piece of fundamental research into the action of burner nozzles and injectors, culminated in the present Flamemaster hand-torch. The list could go on to fill the rest of this book.

Complex and various as it may appear, Chance Research moves steadily, aware of its direction. Its job is to increase efficiency. Its client is the customer.

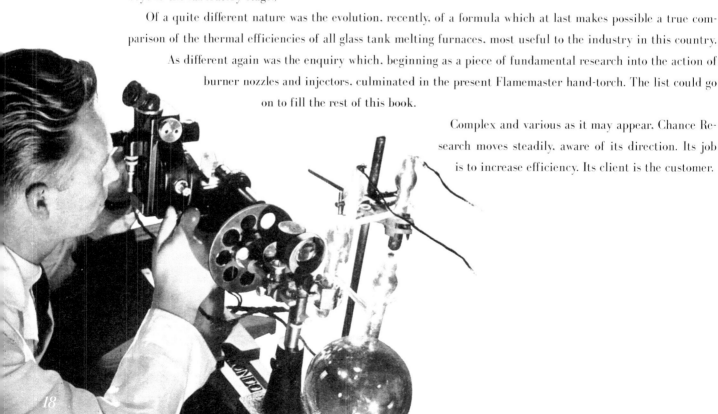

N

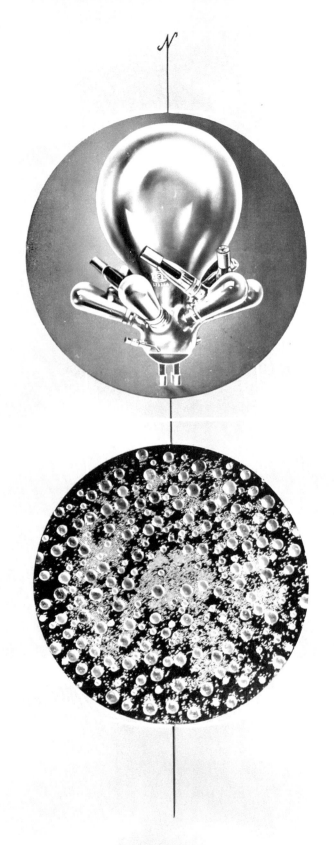

science & industry

Many of the forms of modern laboratory vessels in Hysil heat-resisting glass are still best made by traditional methods

It is significant that the history of Chance Brothers should have coincided with a remarkable period in human history. No other hundred years or so has seen anything like such rapid material progress, such general industrial and scientific advance . . . and to that progress Chance Brothers, as an industrial unit upon an essentially scientific basis, have made important contributions.

In round terms it may fairly be said that for a century and a quarter, as Science and Industry have urged each other forward, Chance Brothers have accompanied them with glass — heat-resistant, acid-resistant, shock-resistant, ray-selective, exceptionally accurate, exceptionally clear or thin, or simply uncommonly handy in design. Without Chance glass the pace would have been slower, the world's achievement less.

Often Chance themselves have shown the way ahead, as with the Truflex mirror for aerodrome lighting, and latterly with the perfection of the all-glass interchangeable hypodermic syringe. As often, scientists and technicians in other industries have called upon Chance to provide the essential element when the need for it arose: instances are to be found in the development of the cathode ray tube, Protex and Protal for eye-protective filters and Calorex light-transmitting heat-absorbing

A fifteen-inch television screen before welding to the body of the tube. The accuracy of this pressing may be judged by the television receiver chassis (with complete tube in position) which can be seen through it.

A Chance ellipsoidal mirror for a cinema projector, mounted in the rear door of a Brockliss lamphouse. These mirrors have to withstand intense heat from the arc source. They have to pick up the light from the positive arc crater and focus it accurately at the film aperture.

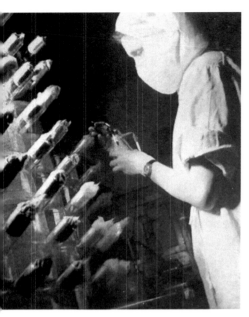

Culture flasks of Hysil glass stand up to high temperature sterilisation. Those shown contain a nutrient jelly which is being inoculated with a bacterial culture

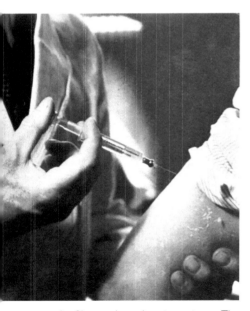

A Chance hypodermic syringe. The gloss barrels and glass plungers of all Chance syringes are manufactured to such fine dimensional limits as to be interchangeable, which greatly simplifies the sterilisation problem in hospitals.

glass. Whether the customer or the Company takes the initiative, in the outcome it is close consultation between them which ensures that the best possible product is designed and manufactured.

There is no one division of Chance Brothers set aside to cater for the needs of Science and Industry (although the Research Laboratory is necessarily much involved). Chance regard such particular orders as all in the day's work—and in any case the scientific prototype of one moment is liable to turn into the large industrial contract of the next. Moreover, these various special products are of very different kinds. Some, like the sunball shown overleaf, are made only in small numbers to a high degree of homogeneity and precision, while others, notably Hysil laboratory ware, are called for in great quantity and standard ranges. Many, therefore, you will find under other headings in this book . . . Optical, Electrical, Lighting.

The two photographs on page 19 epitomize, for the moment, the differences in size and kind which can exist between any two separate pieces of Chance glass in this scientific/industrial field. The upper one shows a mercury arc rectifier (used to convert alternating to direct current) for which Chance create the bulb and separate projecting limbs: this assembly, blown of special Hysil glass for its resistance to local heating, stands four feet high.

The lower illustration shows a collection of the little glass balls known to industry as Ballotini . . . each a perfect sphere, though its diameter may be no greater than 0.092 inch. They are used to provide a brilliant reflecting surface without the effect of a mirror: tiny ones cover the fabric of cinema screens, while larger ones serve on reflecting road signs.

In point of scale, these are the present-day extremes—though how long they will hold their respective positions, who can prophesy! . . . for at any moment Chance might be asked to make something larger, or smaller. And even if Science and Industry were to demand Ballotini as big as pumpkins, or mercury arc rectifiers as small as beads, Chance research would probably discover the answer.

Right: Chance Hysil conical and bolthead flasks stacked ready for despatch; these large flasks are used for distillation and vacuum work. Cathode ray bulbs for television are seen on the top rack. Insets show an operator at Spon Lane 'lipping' a Hysil beaker, and Hysil glassware in use in the laboratories of Glaxo Ltd.

Chance Sunball at Kew Observatory. These perfect spheres of optical glass, four inches in diameter, must be free from all defects or variations in refractive index. In use they are mounted on a stand, with a paper scale behind them facing south: os the sun crosses the sky it bums a track in the scale so long as it is unobscured: the least cloud or haze will make the sun's image too diffused to mark the paper.

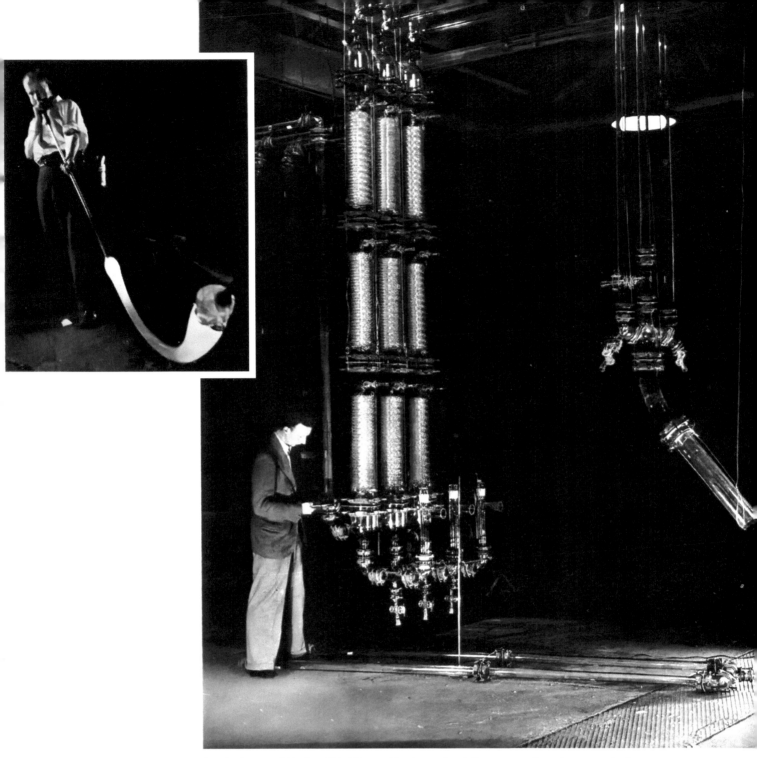

Standard sizes of Hysil and Veridia precision bore glass lulling are mostly made automatically Here Hysil tubing is seen in the construction of a scrubbing tower; the coils in these units act as packed columns, capable of being operated at controlled temperatures.

Above: Hand-drawing Hysil tubing, a highly skilled operation now chiefly used when small quantities and special sizes are required. A muss of glass is first gathered on a pipe, and blown and marvered into a cylinder; an iron rod is then attached to the free end of the cylinder by a dab of hot glass and the second operator walks away from the first, drawing out the lube as he goes.'

25

Chance microscope cover glass is so thin that when a piece the size of an ordinary microscope slide is picked up by one end, it bends like a bow under its own weight (the thinnest is 0.002 inch).

It is made as shown here, by blowing a large sphere and spinning it until it flattens to a hollow disc; careful control of temperature and blowing reduces the front face of this disc to the requisite thinness, when it is finally severed from the rear face by the action of a jet of cold water. The cover slips, (left) seen in use on microscope slides, are cut from the disc when it has cooled.

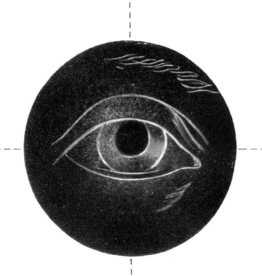

optical and

ophthalmic glass

The photographs on this and the following two pages show the sequence of the normal process at Chance Brothers' St. Helens works.

First, the stirring of the fused ingredients while the crucible is in the furnace (the stirring arm normally enters through a special opening in the furnace door).

Second, the pot of molten glass emerging from the furnace.

Third . . .

For more than one hundred years Chance have been making optical glass to compare with any in the world— a fact which only began to be widely recognized when two world upheavals made it difficult to ignore.

In 1939, for the second time in history, Chance Brothers became the main source in Britain, and also sent supplies throughout the war to the Dominions and the United States. Supplemented by the output from a specially equipped factory at St. Helens they were able to produce all the optical glass that was demanded of them, and more . . . for tank periscopes alone, over a million and a quarter blanks were made (weighing in the rough upwards of a thousand tons of glass), besides great quantities for air camera, rangefinder, binocular, telescope and microscope lenses and prisms.

The recognition won in time of war has been ratified since. Twelve or fifteen years ago export orders were almost non-existent. To-day in many countries Chance have friends and customers who never bought optical glass from Britain before, whilst the contribution made by Chance glass to British optical instruments (for television, cinema and ordinary photography as well as for science) swells the total export figure to quite impressive proportions.

The making of optical glass is an unending search for perfection—for such purity and consistency throughout a solid mass of material as will assure the minimum interference with the passage of light. In such a manufacture it is hardly necessary to emphasize the part played by Chance research—which in recent times has led to some interesting developments, among them certain coloured optical glasses, and others which can only be produced in crucibles of pure platinum.

Research lies behind every stage of every process.

Third, the pouring operation, from a tilting cradle into an iron mould, after which the slab is slowly annealed in a special electric kiln for about four weeks.

Fourth . . .

For certain special glasses platinum pots are now employed. Batches of a hundred pounds or so can be melted in this way in electric resistance furnaces ... the pouring, annealing and subsequent processes are the same as in the case of the larger clay pots.

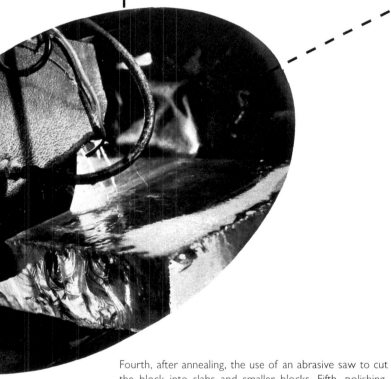

Fourth, after annealing, the use of an abrasive saw to cut the block into slabs and smaller blocks. Fifth, polishing, when small slabs of glass are held on edge by plaster of Paris inside an iron ring, and polished for inspection. Sixth, the weighing of lens and prism blanks for later remoulding in small furnaces to the basic shapes eventually required.

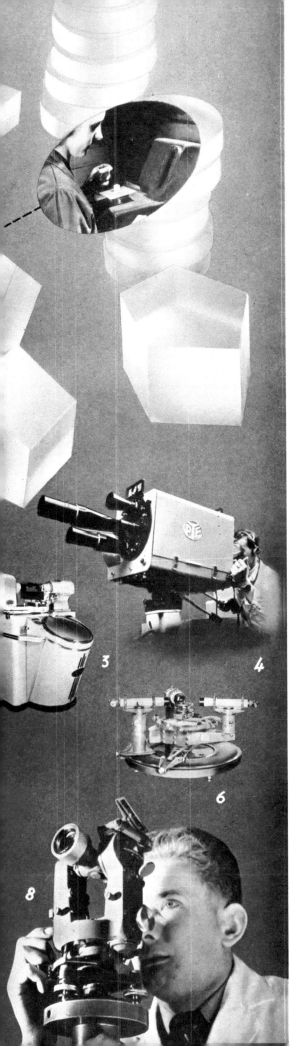

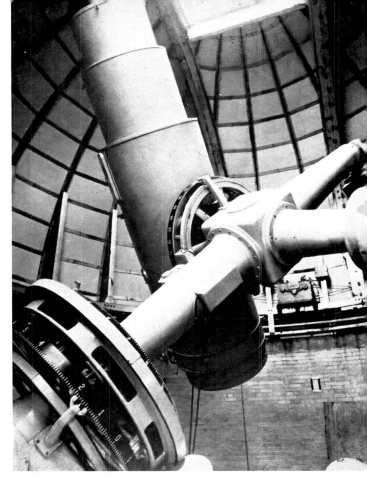

For this great telescope in the observatory of the University of Michigan, U.S.A., Chance Brothers recently made two special prismatic discs of the highest optical quality, each 25½ inches in diameter and averaging 2½ inches thick. They have angles of 4° and 6° respectively, so that, according to the setting, any effective angle between 2° and 10° can be obtained.

The telescope, of the Schmidt type, has an optical system by the Perkin Elmer Corp., of Glenbrook, Connecticut.

Left: All the optical apparatus shown in this composite group relies upon Chance optical glass for lenses or prisms.

1. A Wray-flex 35mm reflex camera (one of very many British cameras using Chance glass).
2. Hilger fully automatic quartz-and-glass spectrograph.
3. Hilger T.500 universal measuring projector.
4. B.B.C. outside-broadcasting television camera.
5. A special hand camera, for taking oblique shots, aimed by one of the crew of a Lysander Army Co-operation plane.
6. N.P.L. spectrometer.
7. A Baker binocular microscope for pathological work.
8. Optical theodolite.

In the field of Ophthalmic Glass (for spectacle lenses and eye protection) Chance Brothers are also important as producers and pioneers. They supply many of the blanks from which spectacle lenses are made and ultimately finished to oculists prescriptions. In the protection of the eye from harmful rays glass plays a different role. its value depending upon its ability to select and filter the incident radiation.

Chance Crookes glass (which gets its name from the collaboration between Chance Brothers and the world-famous physicist Sir William Crookes. O.M.) is now a standard material for cases where protection from intense light is necessary. for better-quality sunglasses and for protection from stray industrial radiation: it has high ultra-violet absorption.

Chance Protex arc filters are glasses specially designed to counter the dangerous rays emitted, during gas welding and electric arc welding. Chance Protal filters do the same job for flux welding. Chance Neodex absorbs the intense yellow rays from the lamp-working of glassware.

lighting glassware

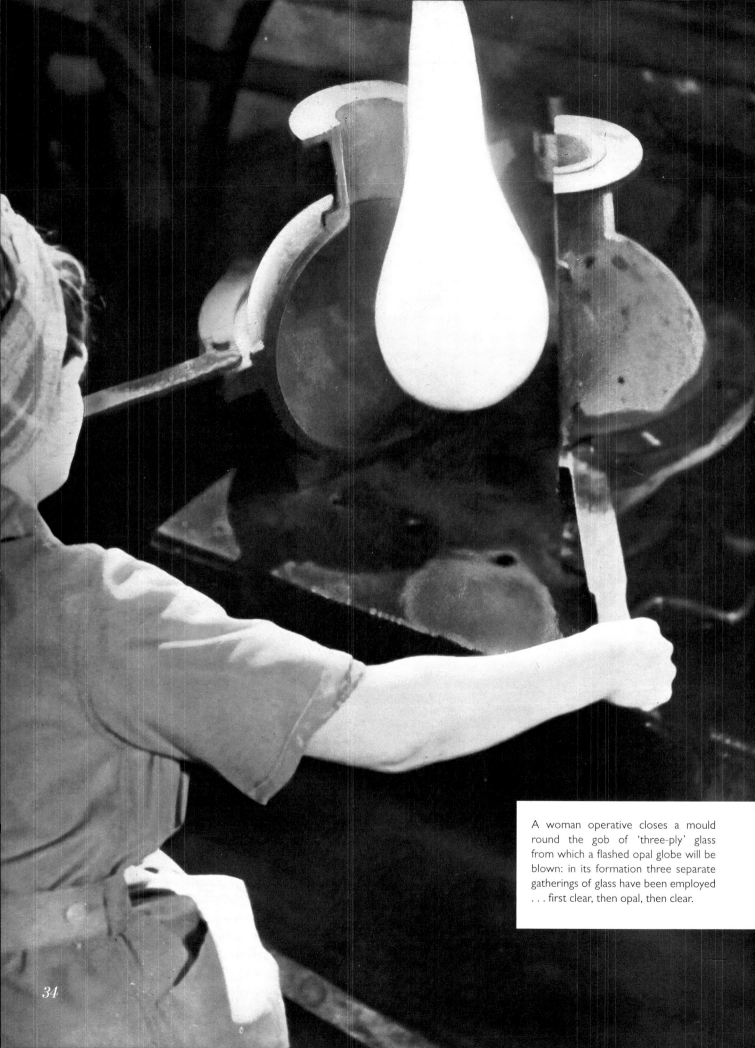

A woman operative closes a mould round the gob of 'three-ply' glass from which a flashed opal globe will be blown: in its formation three separate gatherings of glass have been employed . . . first clear, then opal, then clear.

Electricity

Chance Narrow Reeded glass in a fitting for fluorescent tubes

Every time a new manner of lighting is evolved, Chance come in at an early stage, because modem lighting makes great use of modem glass. And at the same time Chance prepare for a long association—for no new method of illumination ever entirely succeeds in ousting its predecessors.

In shops and offices and factories to-day the trend is fluorescent . . . Chance tubes, in fittings, it may be, of Chance Reeded. Outside in the street, sodium discharge lamps, perhaps, with pressed glass shades by Chance. But, half-a-mile from the highway, a dockside passage is lit with quaint gas lanterns, glazed with Chances' heat-resisting panes . . . half-an-hour from the city a cottage window shows its friendly lamp, the wick surrounded by a tall Chance chimney. Tube or filament, wick or mantle, Chance surrounds them all.

Lights have two familiar functions: they may illuminate other objects, or they may serve as signals. Chance make glass for both kinds. The reds and greens on railway signal gantries are Chance specialities, like the bullseyes for locomotive headlights and the glasses for guards' lamps . . . so are pressed headlamp lenses for motor cars . . . so, needless to say, are the ships' navigation lights, the harbour lights and airfield lights which, on more counts than one, belong to the Chance sphere of activity.

Oil

A Chance Hysil chimney on a modern oil lamp

Gas

Chance Hysil globes for high-pressure street lighting: a standard in Trafalgar Square

35

The use of glass in fluorescent lighting is a matter in which Chance Brothers have paid a lot of attention. They make the tubes for the actual lamps (seen above in simplest form): they also make the decorative glass which in the form of panels or troughs, subdue and diffuse this brilliant lighting to the best advantage.

The large photograph opposite is an example of fluorescent lighting in a decorative scheme for a public room (the Mecca Café in London's Stoll Theatre), where the fitting's are troughs constructed from curved panels of Chance Luminating. The two smaller illustrations show a simple treatment with Chance Narrow Reeded, suitable for an office or passage light, and inset, a businesslike arrangement of unshaded fluorescent tubes in a modern customs sorting shed.

This gathering of flashed glass is being shaped, before being blown into a large cylinder. From the cylinder, when it has been slit and flattened into a sheet, will come signal glass in Chance ruby.

Piccadilly Circus by night. The large lighting globes by Chance replace others which, before the war, were specially imported from America. Below: Any London terminus offers examples of signal lenses, coloured roundels, locomotive lamps, guards' lanterns and a host of station lighting fittings by Chance. Our photograph shows The Night Scot pulling out from King's Cross.

Chance globes and shades for filament lamps are made in great variety (above). The popular spherical shape in flashed opal, shown here in use (top right), is also seen in the hands of a worker who is grinding the rim with an abrasive. Below is another design, photographed in Chance Brothers' offices at St. James's Square, London.

Petrol pump globes (left) in three-ply opal (left) are formed by blowing into moulds shaped according to the pattern.

glass in architecture

The non-stop process which is the manufacture of Chance glass is caught here at four stages in its cycle. First we see the pure white sand which is the basic ingredient . . . next (inset) the chimneys of the melting furnaces which feed two continuous rolling machines, with between them the overhead runway which carries the batch to the automatic feeders . . . then the rollers

The contribution that glass can make to a good building is something more than a means of seeing out of it, important though that is. And, as it happens, plain transparent window glass is a kind Chance Brothers do not make. Their speciality lies in surface texture and pattern which obscure vision without loss of light.

Chance glass plays its part right through a building, carrying daylight where it is wanted. Here in exterior panes, there enclosing a bathroom, an office, a clinical laboratory, or running the length of a passage like a translucent wall . . . here framed in simple panels, there shaped to suit a scheme of decoration . . . in every modern setting you are likely to meet Chance Flashed Opals, Hammered Cathedrals, Flemish, Reeded, Reedlyte and the rest.

Southampton's fine new Ocean Terminal makes use of Chance Cross Reeded glass for windows which require no outside view

at the working end of the continuous machine, through which the molten glass flows to a long conveyor bed for slow cooling . . . Lastly, (200 feet or so away from the rollers) the finished sheet is being cut into lengths by practised hands.

Muranese

Small Glistre

43

Next time you see Big Ben, or hear him on the radio, think of these men, high above Westminster, fitting the face of the great clock with Chance Flashed Opal

Their simplicity of line and effect are in key with present-day ideas. They allow the architect to manipulate light.

So much for the general . . . an idea of the particular must be left to these illustrations. though it should be realized that they can only touch the fringe of the subject. And there is a large demand for all sorts of special Chance products in this field. from Chance wired glass in roof lights to Calorex glass for keeping the heat out of buildings in the tropics . . . for glass roofing tiles. as well. in many shapes and sizes.

Broad Reeded   Broad Reedlyte   Narrow Reeded    Cross Reeded

Chance Major Reeded glass is put to effective use in the tower of an automobile station near Buenos Aires

For over a century Chance Brothers have created coloured Antique glasses for stained glass windows, according to special formulas, many known only to them. Such glass is used for broad areas of colour: the details of portraiture and so on being painted by hand on white glass in metallic pigments (see right) and subsequently fused by firing. The unfinished work shown here is illuminated from behind, with the background roughly darkened to reduce glare.

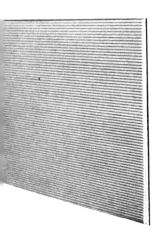

Plain Rolled

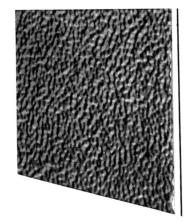

Stippolyte

Rough Cathedral

№ 2 Hammered Cathedral

A very effective interior use of Chance Broad Reeded in screens
and door panels at the London offices of Colgate-Palmolive-Peet Ltd

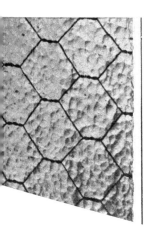

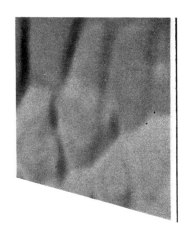

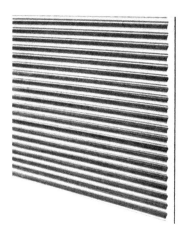

Wired Cast

Large Flemish

Luminating

Packing rolled glass
for road transport
is a skilled job

tableware

On the opposite page, Chance Britannia tableware is partnered by good modern silver . . . it will consort just as naturally with the simplest of pottery and cutlery. Note the sectional hors d'oeuvre dish, the plates large and small, the graceful solidity of the fruit bowl.

THERE are housewives, just possibly, who do not connect the name Chance with lighthouses . . . hotel managers who are unaware of Chance in the world of optical instruments. It may be so. There remains one aspect at least of Chance Glass which can hardly have escaped their attention.

The domestic glassware with which the name of Chance Brothers is associated was a new enterprise only a few years ago. To-day it has an accepted place on thousands of formal and informal tables. And the reason is that before production started Chance made sure that on each of several important points they were able to offer the ordinary everyday user something quite out of the ordinary. First, good (and practical) design by the best glass designers in the country. Second, a wide choice within each design range—and the knowledge that replacements and additions could be depended upon. Third, workaday strength with no hint of clumsiness. Fourth, prices within everybody's reach.

Chance Spiderweb and Waverley tableware, with the more recent Chance Britannia, can be sold to the public at such reasonable figures because, for all their distinction, they are manufactured in bulk by a fully automatic pressing process (which is fascinating to watch). Variety is provided within each range by the addition of ceramic colour, sprayed on or hand applied, and by gold edge-banding or lining. But pressed ware is not always tableware or tableware always pressed—and Chance have new ideas in development which will keep housewives and others interested for a long time to come, as the following pages show.

Left: Stages in the creation of domestic glass:

1. The actual metal mould which conveys the impression to the glass (in this case the Waverley pattern):

2. An automatic fire-polishing machine

3. Inspection of bowls as they come by endless belt from the annealing lehr.

Above: Harry Haller (left) and Percival Goodman discussing a prototype Britannia bowl

Above: A side-table, set with Waverley glass. The jug and tumbler set and salad bowl typify the comfortable roundness of this series.

Right: a more formal arrangement for Chance Spiderweb, which is designed to catch and reflect the light from its concentric facets.

Note: A lack of space forbids the representation in this section of many useful everyday products, such as tumblers, ash trays, refrigerator food boxes and drip trays, which Chance Brothers manufacture as standard lines or to meet specific orders, and of which particulars are readily available.

Fiesta

—AN ANNOUNCEMENT AND A PREVIEW

The photographs on this page are the first ever to be published of a new table glassware by Chance ... Fiesta. Fiesta Glass is not simply different in appearance from anything seen before—behind its easy grace of form and the variety and delicacy of decoration to which it lends itself lies an entirely new process (or rather a series of processes) which Chance Brothers have perfected.

In order to appreciate its full beauty from these few examples (which can do no more than hint at the range of developments to come), imagination must supply the rich tones of the glass . . . the intricate arabesques and vignettes in gold. in black. in any colour under the sun . . . the curious subtlety of the curves. deep and shallow . . . the unexpected lightness of each object in the hand . . . Fiesta has great charm. a sort of quintessential luxury. Yet it is as practical and usable as any housewife could desire.

And it will not be expensive.

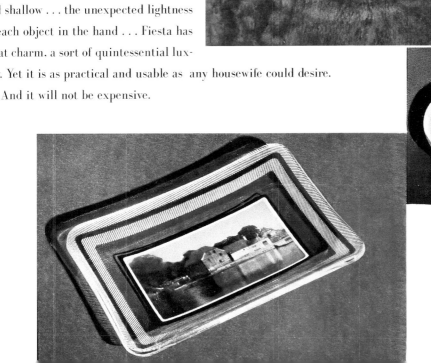

Chance Lights the Seaways of the World

On this world map are recorded many marine navigational lights which Chance Brothers have installed since the foundation of their Lighthouse Works in the year 1851.

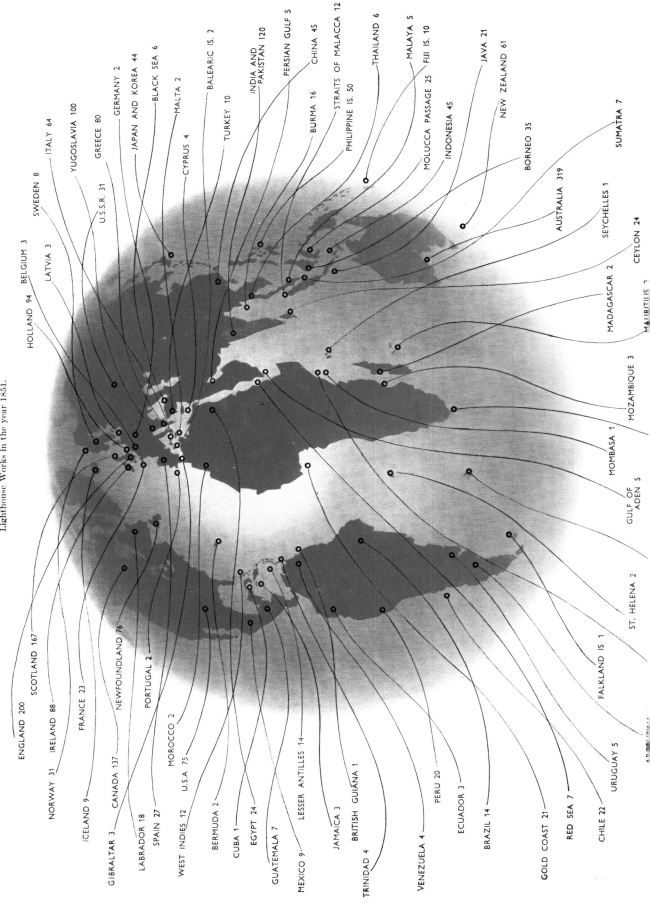

ENGLAND 200
SCOTLAND 167
IRELAND 88
FRANCE 23
NEWFOUNDLAND 76
PORTUGAL 2
MOROCCO 2
U.S.A. 75
BERMUDA 2
CUBA 1
EGYPT 24
LESSER ANTILLES 14
BRITISH GUIANA 1
VENEZUELA 4
PERU 20
ECUADOR 3
BRAZIL 14
FALKLAND IS 1
ST. HELENA 2
URUGUAY 5
RED SEA 7
CHILE 22
GOLD COAST 21
TRINIDAD 4
JAMAICA 3
GUATEMALA 7
MEXICO 9
WEST INDIES 12
SPAIN 27
LABRADOR 18
CANADA 137
GIBRALTAR 3
ICELAND 9
NORWAY 31

HOLLAND 94
BELGIUM 3
LATVIA 3
SWEDEN 8
U.S.S.R. 31
YUGOSLAVIA 100
GREECE 80
ITALY 64
GERMANY 2
JAPAN AND KOREA 44
BLACK SEA 6
MALTA 2
CYPRUS 4
TURKEY 10
BALEARIC IS. 2
INDIA AND PAKISTAN 120
PERSIAN GULF 5
BURMA 16
CHINA 45
STRAITS OF MALACCA 12
PHILIPPINE IS. 50
THAILAND 6
MALAYA 5
FIJI IS. 10
MOLUCCA PASSAGE 25
INDONESIA 45
JAVA 21
NEW ZEALAND 61
BORNEO 35
AUSTRALIA 319
SUMATRA 7
SEYCHELLES 1
CEYLON 24
MADAGASCAR 2
MOZAMBIQUE 3
MOMBASA 1
GULF OF ADEN 5
MAURITIUS 3

52

marine & aviation

Though Chance Brothers date their Lighthouse Works from the year 1851, you would, as a matter of fact, have to look a few years earlier for the beginning of the story. It is to Sir James Timmins Chance in the first place that credit is due for the Company's pre-eminence in this special field, and after him to his chosen successor at Spon Lane, Dr. John Hopkinson, the celebrated electrical engineer. Between them these two were responsible for hundreds of installations in the '60s and '70s, at places as far apart as Gibraltar, New Zealand and Mexico . . . starting points in a world-wide pattern which the map on page 52 can do no more than summarize to-day.

Once such an industry became known (in an age of coastlines grievously under equipped), its rapid extension was not so much surprising as necessary. Similarly with its internal development. Thus glass led to optical systems, thence to frameworks, to illuminants, to the mechanics of movement and group- flashing. Thus, moreover, sealights led in the fullness of time to airlights. The mobile "Chancelights" of the second World War, the latest square-beamed location beacons . . . these and their like are just as much in the direct succession as are all the buoys and harbour lights and ships' signal lights which Chance Brothers have made in a hundred years.

Glass being glass, and light being light, the fundamental optical principles upon which James Timmins Chance and his colleagues based their calculations and operations have never become outdated, while by contrast the mechanical and in particular the electrical side has seen surprising advances. You are often struck by this contrast, as you walk round the Lighthouse Works at Spon Lane . . .

WOLF ROCK LIGHTHOUSE

As equipped by Chance in 1869, the Wolf Rock bore a revolving red-and-white light with an oil wick illuminant: this has since been changed to a white 70,000-candle beam by petrol vapour. The original optical system (described at the time as "probably the most perfect yet constructed") is still in use.

THE 'EYE' OF A LIGHTHOUSE

Top right: Inspecting the reflecting prisms of a 3rd-order optic. Before it is finally sealed into position, each prism must be individually focused . . .

. . . and each, by the time it is ready for assembly, has been through a grinding and polishing operation which may have taken as long as a fortnight. The spherical surface to this glass ring is produced by rocking the arm which carries the grinding pad, as the ring rotates.

In one shop craftsmen are fashioning by hand and eye the frame for a 4th-order optic, or a wind vane with a fine bronze arrow. In another, curved prisms are rotating on a polishing machine according to a system first devised in the 1860s. In a third you watch the assembly of modern electrical generating equipment, automatic and self-sufficient, which can control a flashing light for weeks at a stretch without human supervision—a robot lighthouse-keeper. The oldest and the newest keep step here, on the unsentimental basis of efficiency.

This Chance buoy will run day and night for a minimum of fourteen weeks on acetylene which in stored in cylinders fitted into pockets on the body. Lens and flasher (shown separately on page 58) are Chance specialities. Fitted above is a radar reflector by which the buoy may be recognised in fog by ships fitted with radar scanners.

READY FOR ITS DESTINATION

The final inspection at Spon Lane of a 5th-order rotating optic with electric motor drive. Two motors are installed: if one fails the other starts automatically, picking up the drive through a centrifugal clutch as it reaches full speed . . .

. . . A similar apparatus was installed in 1931 at the Macquarie Lighthouse, Australia, to replace an electric-arc 1st-order light of 1882.

This automatic flashing device for an acetylene buoy is operated by the pressure of the gas itself, which overcomes a restraining spring at regular intervals

Automatic lamp-changers such as these immediately replace a burnt-out bulb by moving a standby into the correct focal position

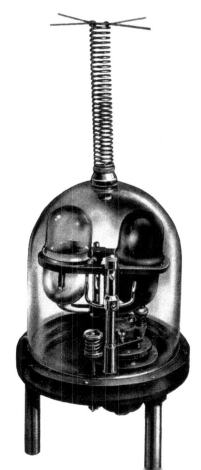

On unattended beacons, these automatic light-valves turn on the light at dusk or whenever the daylight drops below a certain intensity. Unlike the photocell, they require no electric supply, but operate through the volatility of ether. The flexible spring on top is a booby-trap to discourage perching gulls, whose droppings would obscure the light

THE CHANCE DIAPHONE

An important development, this, of Chance lighthouse engineering . . . for when lights cannot be seen, as in conditions of fog, sounds must take their place.

For a number of reasons, the Diaphone is regarded by competent authorities all over the world as one of the very best sound-signals for aiding navigation at sea. Its mechanism is basically simple, robust in construction and easy to maintain. By means of a slotted piston-head moving 90 complete cycles per second in a correspondingly slotted cylinder, the passage of air is interrupted 180 times per second, producing a steady and immediate note, with none of the preliminary surging wail characteristic of many sirens. The volume is tremendous: in favourable conditions audible ranges of over forty miles have been reported.

Right: The Chance Diaphone installation at Dungeness Lighthouse—note that in this case two horns are employed, angled so as to give a wide range of sound distribution.

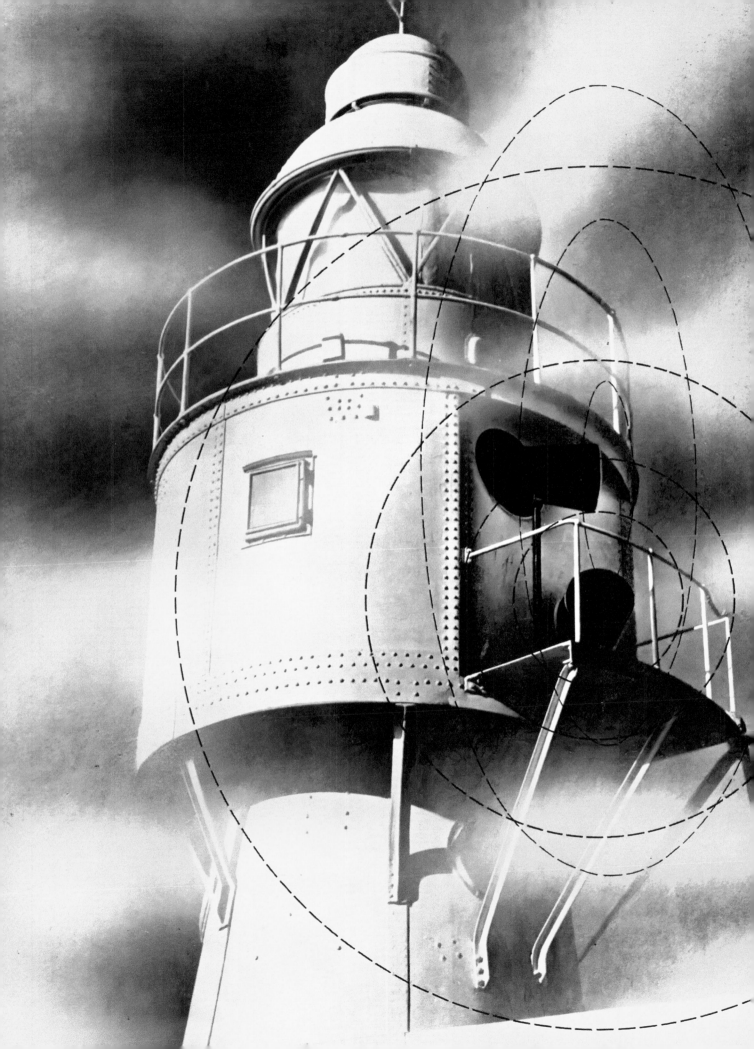

THE CHANCE SQUARE-BEAM AIRPORT BEACON

In the air the question of recognition is fully as important as at sea. Pilots have known Chance navigational lighting in many forms during and before the war years—to-day, on routes which circle the world, they watch for the reassuring flash of Chance Brothers' famous square-beam airport location beacons.

By international agreement the signal for land airports is an alternate white and green flash, for sea airports white and yellow, and the integrated intensity of the white light must be not less than 100,000 of the green and yellow 15,000 candle seconds. The performance of the Chance square-beam beacon can be judged from its comparative figures, which are 300,000 candle seconds of white light, 60,000 of green and 150,000 of yellow, *with constant flash duration to the upper limit of the angle of view.*

This square-beam airport beacon is a lively hint of Chance Brothers' plans towards the greater safety and dependability of air and sea travel.

electrical products

THE SUMO PUMP

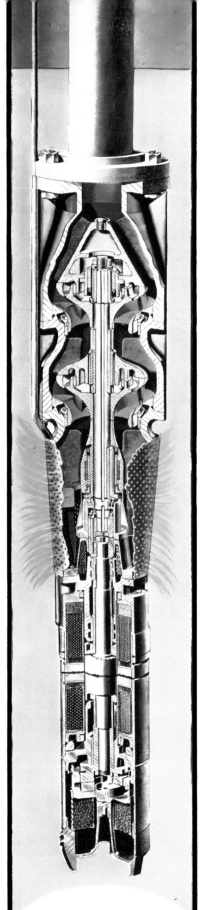

ITS BACKGROUND

Chance engineering, specialist and selective, springs from lighthouse interests. As Chance Brothers steadily perfected their light systems, they came to rely more and more upon their own engineering inventiveness, because equipment of the required precision and dependability frequently didn't exist until they had made it for themselves.

Out of all this experience grew the modern Engineering Division of Chance Brothers. And from the Engineering Division sprang the Chance specialist subsidiary, Sumo Pumps Ltd.

ITS PRINCIPLES

The Sumo Submersible has been described as "the pump that gets down to it." And that is the whole thing in a nutshell. Instead of separating pump from motor, and then filling the borehole with shafting and bearings in order to connect them again, the Sumo, motor-and-pump in one cigar-shaped unit, goes down to the bottom of the well on the end of the delivery pipe and works under water.

The idea is simple, but it depends upon faultless engineering.

The Sumo pump would not be possible without the Sumo motor (a squirrel-cage AC motor expressly designed to work under water for long periods without attention) to which the pump itself is direct-coupled.

ITS ADVANTAGES

A Sumo Submersible Pump, therefore, requires no foundation, no pump-house, no shafting and only the smallest of boreholes; on ground level nothing need show but a man-hole lid. Quick and inexpensive to install, its cost becomes relatively more and more favourable for every foot of bore.

Running is economical and efficient. Priming troubles cannot arise. Suction troubles do not exist. Maintenance is as simple as installation.

There are types of Sumo available now to give any quantity of water between 300 and 60,000 gallons per hour, and this range is increasing.

Section through a typical Sumo Pump, showing the motor and waterways.

Gauging a Sumo shaft during grinding. Right: The dynamic balancing of the complete shaft and impeller assembly. Great accuracy in all operations is the reason for the Sumo's low wear and vibrationless running at high speeds, while very fine clearances protect bearings from grit

Winding a stator for a type KL motor. The finished winding will be sealed by a thin stainless steel tube, inside which water will be free to circulate around the rotor. Right: Assembling the final stage of a Type E Sumo pump

Below: A before and after story. The picture on the left shows an old reciprocating pump working in its pump hole at a Middlesex pumping station. The one on the right shows the rising main and valve—all that can be seen—of the Sumo Type E pump which replaced it

Austinlite Ltd. another Chance subsidiary. has even more common ground with the parent company than Sumo. For the great sea lights that Chance construct must have generating plant which can be trusted never to fail . . . and since. in industry. in the public services. in hospital work (to take only three examples). there are also circumstances when' an electrical breakdown would be a disaster. Chance Brothers have made their knowledge readily available through the Austinlite Service.

Austinlite automatic standby generating equipment is now looked upon as a routine precaution in many a factory. hotel. theatre or nursing home which used to depend entirely upon the continuance of the public supply. Austinlite generators are installed in G.P.O. Repeater Stations. For airfields. and other duties where only a few seconds of darkness might be fatal. Austinlite provide continuous-running plant which will take over without even a momentary interruption should a mains failure occur.

In addition. they make a number of special components. designed in the first place to meet their own exacting requirements. and now placed on the open market. Seen above are the Austinlite 'Fifty' and 'Thirty heavy-duty rotary switches. the Austinlite rotary meter switch with unvarying contact resistance. and a marginal relay which serves either as a contacting ammeter or voltmeter.

An automatic 150 Kw Austinlite generating plant driven by a 250 h.p. oil engine. The generator is separately excited, and controlled by an auto-voltage regulator, enclosed in the triangular guard at the nearer end.

Testing an Austinlite power switchboard for a telephone repeater station.

65

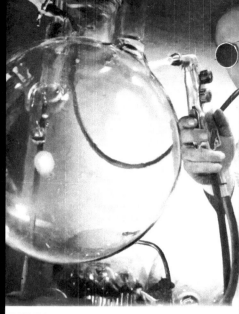

FLAMEMASTER & BORNKESSEL

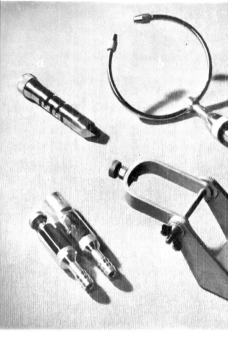

Though the Chance-Bornkessel burners and the Flamemaster Torch are not electrical, they come into this section by the logic of convenience—and because they, too, are typical products of Chance engineering, evolved for and tested in the Glass Works before they were offered to the public.

Wherever directed flame-heating is required on work-bench or machine, there is a Bornkessel burner to provide it . . . essentially for glass working, potentially for anything from hard-soldering to brazing or welding. Designed to burn coal gas with air or with oxygen, the series includes single and dual purpose, crossfire, ribbon and remelting burners of proven usefulness.

More versatile still is the Flamemaster Hand Torch, which owes its efficiency to basic research into the principles of controlled flames, plus design for maximum convenience. An all-purpose torch, burning coal gas, hydrogen or butane with compressed air or oxygen, the Flamemaster embodies a number of interchangeable flame units which, together with its quick-action needle valves and thumb controls, make it as valuable for the jeweller as it is for the general engineer. A characteristic is the built-in, leakproof economiser, which cuts off the gas and air supplies when the operator's grip is released, and restores the flame when the torch is held in the hand. The whole torch weighs only fourteen ounces.

Top: A Flamemaster hand torch in use for sealing a limb into a vacuum flask (the operator is blowing through a rubber tube in order to maintain a slight pressure inside the vessel).

Centre: Flamemaster fitments: (a) Soldering bolt—which converts the torch into a soldering iron with close heat control; (b) Double tipping-and-sealing attachment; (c) Oxygen-air mixer; (d) Bench clamp.

Bottom: Fitting a side tube to a distillation flask, using a Bornkessel bench burner.

THE SOLID THAT'S A LIQUID

Everybody knows what glass is. How many would care to define it? Scientifically speaking, the word can refer to any one of a whole range of substances which differ from each other in chemical composition and physical properties, yet which share an essential characteristic . . . that of having cooled from a molten to a solid state without crystallizing.

To put it another way, glass at room temperature can be regarded *as a liquid of such high viscosity that it behaves as a solid.*

Common to glass as most people know it, and as Chance make it, is the staple ingredient silica, or sand. Other elements may be added to determine the nature of the glass, but the right kind of sand is the first requirement, and often a difficult one to fulfil. Our only native supply suitable for optical glass, for instance, is a mine at Loch Aline in Argyllshire, and the importance of that particular deposit lies chiefly in the lowness of its iron content—for all natural sands contain iron, cause of the familiar green tinge in beer bottles and glass marbles.

The first stage in the manufacture of glass is to prepare the 'batch', which consists of a carefully regulated mixture of new raw materials (sand and chemical compounds) called 'frit', with broken glass from previous makings, called 'cullet'. This mixture is introduced into a furnace at temperatures which range between 1,300 and 1,600 degrees Centigrade: reactions occur between the raw materials as they melt, and large quantities of gas are evolved, until a stage is reached at which they become a glowing, heaving, viscous mass, full of bubbles which rise to the surface and escape. A glance through the inspection port of a big tank furnace is as good an introduction as any to Dante's *Inferno*.

Once the contents of a furnace have reached the required condition, they are ready for fabrication by blowing, pressing, pouring, rolling or drawing: and here the long history of the glass industry keeps overlapping itself. For all these processes are now performed automatically in large-scale production, having been evolved from their hand counterparts—yet the earlier hand methods have never been entirely supplanted, so important is human skill in certain operations. Thus hand-blowing and mechanical blowing flourish at the same time, whilst continuous production presses (such as the rotating robots which fashion Chance Britannia and Spiderweb tableware) imitate the skilled worker at his hand press in the neighbouring shop.

The human operative works from a pot furnace, a single crucible (though it is generally one of a battery) which is filled, heated and opened as a cycle of operations. The machine works from a tank furnace, drawing a continuous supply of molten glass through rollers or down a feeder from the working end, while the tank is automatically replenished with fresh raw materials fed in at the other end.

At each pot furnace a 'gatherer', as he is called, takes a gathering of glass from the mouth of the furnace on a gathering-iron or 'punty', or it may be on a pipe which he hands to the blower (master, incidentally, of an art invented by the Romans in the early Christian era). The men work, smoothly and expertly, in teams of two or three. The machine is its own gatherer, its own fabricator, and the products as they leave it are often carried on automatically through further processes, such as annealing, or controlled cooling to eliminate internal stresses which would otherwise occur.

Those are the basic principles of glass manufacture, though there are many variations for special products such as optical glass. The process chosen in each case by Chance Brothers is the one which gives the highest efficiency—and the trend, needless to say, is towards automatic production, with its greater output, lower costs and prices.

But if hand processes die hard, so does the ancient language of glassmaking . . . Cullet, batch, punty . . . the business bristles with such terms. Here are a few more of the most usual (or unusual):—

Bail: The tool dipped into molten glass to start any drawing operation.

Boot: A suspended enclosure in the nose of a tank which serves as a gathering opening.

Brown's Nose: A cast-iron tool used for levering up pots.

Chevally: A rack for holding glass articles when warm; sometimes called a Horse.

Chunks: Random sizes of glass sheets which are smaller than standard.

Crizzle: An imperfection in the form of a fine surface fracture.

Doghouse: A small box-like vestibule on a furnace, into which the batch is fed.

Eye: The opening which the flame enters at the bottom of a pot furnace.

Feathers: An imperfection, consisting of clusters of fine bubbles, caused by dust or foreign matter in the glass.

Glory Hole: A heated cylindrical hole, used to keep a 'gathering' of glass warm during processing.

Gob: A portion of hot glass (generally as delivered by an automatic feeder).

Lehr: A long tunnel-shaped oven for annealing glass by continuous passage.

Marver: A flat plate on which a hand gather of glass is rolled, shaped and cooled.

Moil: The waste glass remaining on a punty or blowpipe after use.

Monkey: A small pot furnace.

Neddying Hole: A hole in the side of a furnace for running off surplus metal from broken pots.

Nose: The working end of a tank.

Parison: A preliminary shape or blank from which a glass article is to be formed.

Pig: A rest for blowpipe or punty during the gathering operation.

Putty: A white polishing compound.

Seed: An extremely small bubble in glass.

Siege: The floor of a pot furnace (also called 'bench').

Sweet: Term applied to easily workable glass.

Teaser: The worker in charge of a furnace operation who regulates the introduction of batch and adjusts the temperature.

Teeming: Another term for casting.

Tweel (tuille): A counter-weighted furnace door, opening vertically.

A vocabulary like this can have its surprises for the outsider. Once, when the Chairman of Chance Brothers was entertaining a particularly pompous visitor, an untidy head was thrust round his door.

"Sir!" said a voice. "Sir! . . shall I whitewash the monkey?"

MADE BY THE CHANCE GROUP

A reference list of the different glass and engineering products manufactured
by Chance Brothers Limited at Smethwick. Glasgow. St Helens and Malvern

A

Acetylene Marine Lighting Equipment
Airport Lighting Equipment
Location Beacons
Antique Glass
Are-Lamp Glasses (for photo-copying)
Are-Screen Glass (Protex and Protal)
Ashtrays
Austinlite Relays
    ..   Rotary Switches
    ..   Control Switchgear
    ..   Automatic Generating Plant
Automatic Lamp Exchangers

B

Ballotini (Glass Beads)
Beacons. Airport
Beacons and Buoys (Dissolved Acetylene)
Bent Glass (clear. opal and coloured)
Boiler Gauge Glasses
Bornkessel Burners
Britannia range of Domestic Glassware
Building Glasses
Bulkhead Glasses

C

Calorex Heat-absorbing Glass
Cathedral Glass (for building)
Cathode Ray Tube Envelopes
Chimneys (for oil lamps)
Coffee Percolator Glasses
Coloured Sheet Glass (ruby. blue. yellow. green and
    opal)
Colour Filter Glasses (for optical purposes)
Condenser Lenses (for film studio lighting)
Condenser Lens Blanks (plate glass)
Cover Glasses (for indicator panels ami switchboards)
Cover Slips (for microscope slides)
Crookes Glass Blanks (eye-protective)
Cylinders (for lighting and industrial purposes)

D

Decklight and Skylight Glasses
Deep Well Pumps
Diaphone Fog Signals
Discs (heat-resisting glass. soft glass)
Domestic Glassware (pressed). clear and decorated

E

Electric Lighting Globes and Shades
    ..   Marine Lighting Apparatus
    ..   Submersible Pumps
Ellipsoidal Arc Mirrors (for projectors)
Eye-protecting Glasses (Crookes. Protex. Protal and
    Neodex)

F

Fiesta range of Domestic Glassware
Figured Glasses (for Building)
Flamemaster Hand Torches
Flashed Opal Glass (white and coloured)
Flemish Glass (for building) fluorescent Lighting Fit-
    ting Panels Fog Signals. Marine

G

Gas-Air/Gas-Air-Oxygen Burners
    ..   Buoys. Lanterns and Lenses
    ..   Lighting Globes and Shades
Generating Plant. Austinlite
Globes. Lighting (clear. opal and coloured)

H

Heat-absorbing Glass (Calorex)
Heat-absorbing. Heat-resisting Glass—ON20
Heat-resisting Sheet Glass
Hysil Heat-resisting Glass
    ..   Heat-resisting Laboratory Glassware
    ..   Tubing and Rod

I

Industrial Glass Equipment

L

Laboratory Tubing (Hysil)
    ..   Beakers. Flasks. etc. (Hysil)
    ..   Microscope Cover Slips and Slides
    ..   Watch and Clock Glasses
    ..   Petri Dishes
Lamp Exchangers. Automatic
Lens Blanks (optical glass)
Lenses (clear and coloured)
    ..   Bull's-eye. for railway lamps
    ..   Condenser. for film studio lighting
    ..   Dioptric. for ships' navigation lights
    ..   for aerodrome lighting
    ..   for motor headlamps
    ..   for pavement lights
    ..   for road traffic signals
    ..   Stepped. for railway signalling

L

Lighthouse Lanterns and Associated Equipment
    ..   Lighting Equipment, etc.
    ..   Optics, fixed and revolving
Lighting Glassware, clear and coloured, for electricity, gas and oil (for interior use, street lighting, aerodromes, etc.)

M

Marginal Relays
Marine Lighting Equipment
    ..   Fog Signals
Microscope Cover Slips and Slides
Milking Machine Glasses

N

Nailsea Cathedral Glass (for building)
Neodex Glass (eye-protective) for glass welding

O

Oil Lamp Chimneys
    ..   Pressure Relays
Opal Lighting Glass (white and coloured)
Ophthalmic Glass Blanks
Optical Glass, moulded or in slabs

P

Pavement Lenses
Petri Dishes
Petrol Pump Globes
Pipettes, syringe
Port lights and Leading Lights
Powdered Glass and Tinsel
Prism Blanks (optical glass)
Protal Glasses (eye-protective) for gas welding with flux
Protex Glasses (eye-protective) for gas and electric welding
Pumps, Electric, Sumo

R

Rectifier Bulbs
Reeded and Reedlyte Glass (for building)
Reflectors, clear and silvered
Refrigerator Food Boxes and Drip Trays
Relays, Austinlite
Rod, heat-resisting (Hysil)
Rolled Building Glasses (Figured, Cathedral, Reeded, etc.)

Rolled and Coloured Sheet for lighting
Roofing Glass, wired and unwired
Rotary Switches, Austinlite

S

Series Voltage Regulators
Ships' Navigation Lights, Lenses for
Signal Glasses (ruby, green and yellow)
Skylight and Decklight Glasses
Slates, glass
Spectacle Glasses (Crookes, white and bifocal (tints)—moulded or dropped blanks, or sheet
Spiderweb range of Domestic Glassware
Square Beam Airport Location Beacons
Stained Glass Windows, glass for
Standby Plant, Automatic
Stippolyte Glass (for building)
Studio Condenser Lenses
Sumo Submersible Pumps
Sunshine Recorder Spheres
Syringes, all glass, with interchangeable plungers

T

Telescope Lens and Mirror Blanks (optical glass) Test Tubes
Tiles, glass (bent)
Tinsel and Powdered Glass
Traffic Signal Lenses
Tubing, heat-resisting for laboratory use (Hysil)
    ..   precision bore (Veridia)
    ..   sealing glass
    ..   soda-lime for fluorescent   lamps
Tumblers

V

Veridia Precision Bore Glass Tubing
Voltage Regulators (series)

W

Waverley range of Domestic Glassware
Welders' Eye-protecting Glasses (Protex and Protal)
Well Glasses
White Plate Glass Lens Mouldings
Wired Cast Glass (for building)

X

X-ray Bulbs

THE FOLLOWING IS A LIST OF TRADEMARKS REGISTERED BY CHANCE BROTHERS LIMITED:

ACTINEX, AQUALUX, CALOREX, FUSALYTE, HYSIL, INTASIL, MONTENE, PROTAL, PROTEX, SCINTILLA, SOLAREX, SELENALYTE, STIPPOLYTE, SUMO (SUMO PUMPS LTD), SUMONO (SUMO PUMPS LTD), TRUVEX, TRUFLEX, VERIDIA

OUR LONDON OFFICE – *how to get there*

Five minutes walk from Piccadilly Circus . . . three from St. James's Street . . . one from Pall Mall . . . If you're further afield than this map shows, you simply hail a taxi saying

"28, ST. JAMES'S SQUARE!"

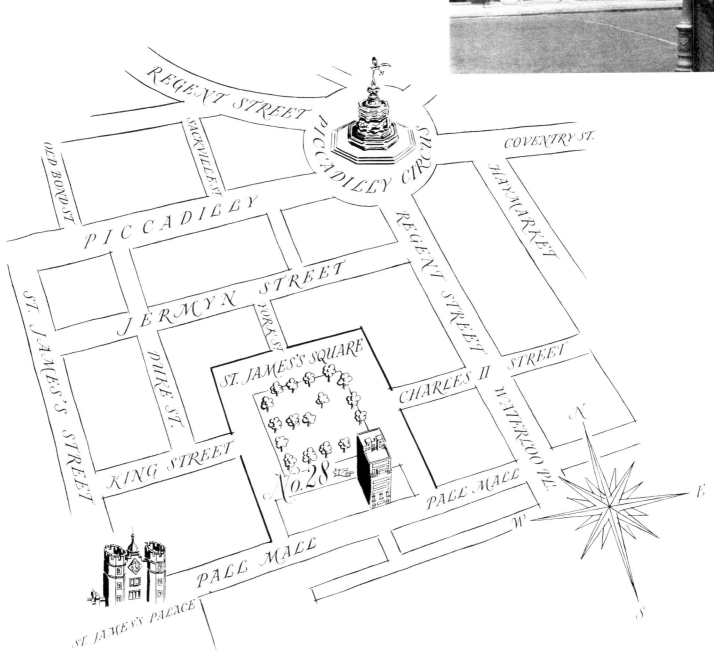

WITH PLEASURE

With pleasure we refer to the assistance which we have received from many quarters in securing illustrations for this book. While it is impossible to mention every instance, we should like to make the following specific acknowledgments:—

To the Editor and Publishers of Future for permission to base the chart on page 11 on an original of which they hold the copyright: to the Electric Construction Co. Ltd., for the photograph of a mercury arc rectifier on page 19: to Ferranti Ltd. one of whose television sets is shown on page 21: to Glaxo Laboratories Ltd. for photographs on pages 22 (top) and 23 (inset): to Quickfit & Quartz Ltd. for photographs of equipment (page 25) and eye-protection (page 32): to the University of Michigan for the print of the telescope on page 31: to Pye Ltd. Keystone Press Agency Ltd. Wray (Optical Works) Ltd. Hilger & Watts Ltd and Charles Baker of Holborn Ltd. for photographs of optical apparatus on the same page: to Thorn Electrical Industries Ltd. (page 36): to Thorn Electrical Industries Ltd. and Mecca Ltd., for the photograph of the Stoll Theatre Cafe on page 37: to the Architectural Review for page 37 (inset): to Planet News Ltd. and Fox Photos Ltd. respectively for the large and small pictures of Big Ben on page 44: to the Daily Graphic for their air photograph of the Wolf Rock Lighthouse on page 54.

In addition, we are indebted to the following for facilities to take photographs on their premises:— Warner Theatre Ltd. Leicester Square. London and J. Frank Brockliss Ltd (a cinema arc mirror in use): the Air Ministry (sunball at Kew Observatory): United States Lines (fluorescent lighting fitting on page 35): British Railways and the Station Master at King's Cross (night view at that station): A. K. Nicholson Stained Glass Studios (stained glass window): Colgate-Palmolive-Peet Ltd (interior view of their offices): Brown Lennox & Co. Ltd (buoy on page 56): the Corporation of Trinity House (Diaphone installation at Dungeness), the Commonwealth Lighthouse Service of Australia (Macquarie Lighthouse): Pick Hill Pumping Station Ltd (a pump installation.)

Photographs taken specially at our Works at Smethwick. St. Helens. Glasgow and elsewhere are by Shaw Wildman. Neil Nimmo. Walter Nurnberg. Bertram Follett. Raymond C. Wilson. Millar & Harris. Derek Beck and George Parmiter.

1951

The original book was written and designed for Chance Brothers Ltd. by Cecil D. Notley Advertising Ltd.
The text is set in Monotype 10 pt. Modern. captions in 8 pt. Bodoni Heavy and 8 pt. Gill Medium.
Printers: Th os. Forman & Sons Ltd.
Engravers: John Swain & Sons Ltd.

2022

This reprint was edited and reimagined for the Chance Heritage Trust. by David Encill.
The text is set in Bodoni 10 pt.
Captions in 9 pt. Gill Medium.
Printers: Printondemand-worldwide.

CHANCE BROTHERS LIMITED

Chance

HEAD OFFICE	Glass Works, Smethwick 40, Birmingham.
	Telephone: West Bromwich 1051.
	Telegrams and Cables: Chance Telex Smethwick.
	Lighthouse Works, Smethwick 40, Birmingham.
	Telephone: West Bromwich 1051.
	Telegrams and Cables: Lightship Telex Smethwick.
LONDON OFFICE	28 St. James's Square, London, S.W.1.
	Telephone: Whitehall 1603.
SCOTLAND	Glass Works, Firhill, Glasgow, N.W.
	Telephone: Maryhill 2141. Telegrams: Brogan Glasgow.
LANCASHIRE	Umbroc Works, St. Helens, Lancs.
	Telephone: St. Helens 4001.
WORCESTERSHIRE	Engineering Section, Pickersleigh Road, Malvern, Worcs.
	Telephone: Malvern 1806.
	Optical Section: Pickersleigh Avenue, Malvern, Worcs.
	Telephone: Malvern 168.

AUSTINLITE LIMITED

Austinlite

	Lighthouse Works, Smethwick 40, Birmingham.
	Telephone: West Bromwich 1051.
	Telegrams: Austinlite Lighthouse Works Smethwick
	Cables: Austinlite Smethwick.

SUMO PUMPS LIMITED

HEAD OFFICE	Lighthouse Works, Smethwick 40, Birmingham.
	Telephone: West Bromwich 1051.
	Telegrams & Cables: Sumo Smethwick
	Cables: Austinlite Smethwick.
USA	Sumo Pumps Inc., 1 Atlantic Street, Stamford, Connecticut.
	Telephone: Stamford 3-0668.
	Telegrams and Cables: Sumopump Stamford.